The stories at this level

The stories at this level are more varied in complex plots. The West Street characters, centre of the stories, and thus give children familiarity.

CW00342774

There are more legends and traditional stories at this level, some of which are in verse, as it is important that children should relish and enjoy the rhythms and sound patterns of rhymes, even if they do not understand every word.

The stories begin to go beyond children's everyday experiences by introducing fantasy and life in the past. This will help to extend your child's horizons; you may want to make direct comparisons between your child's experiences and what happens to the other people in the stories.

Before you start reading with your child, read the story and activities first yourself, so that you become familiar with the text and the best way to give it expression and emphasis when reading it aloud.

Always sit comfortably with your child, so that both of you can see the book easily.

Read the story to your child, making it sound as interesting as possible. Encourage your child to participate actively in the reading, to turn over the pages and to become involved in the story and characters.

If your child seems confident, you may miss out your own first reading. Suggest that you read the story together the first time. Carry your child's reading along with your own, without slowing up or losing fluency or expression. Do this again, but tell your child that you will stop reading when you get a signal (for example a push on the arm), and will start reading again when given another signal. Then say "Do you want to read the story all on your own now?"

Finish by asking if you should read the whole story again to your child. Then say "Now you might like to go away and read the story to yourself (or to Teddy or a younger brother or sister) when you feel like it."

The activities at this level

The activities need not be completed at once. They are not a test, but will help your child to remember the words and stories and to develop further the skills required for becoming a fluent reader.

The activities are often divided into three parts.

One part is designed to encourage discussion about the stories, and to link them where possible with the child's own experiences. Encourage your child to predict what will happen and to recall the main events of the story. Change the wording of the story as much as you like and encourage your children to tell you about the story in their own way.

One part encourages children to look back through the book to find general or specific things in the text or the pictures. The child learns to begin to look at the text itself, and to recognise individual words and letters more precisely. The activities state clearly when you should give a letter its name, and when you should sound it out. The activities also introduce more writing, largely copying from words in the original story. If your children find this too difficult, copy the words onto a piece of paper for them to trace over.

One part is headed *Things to do* and consists of activities which your child can do without your help. You may have to read the instructions for the activities first. Suggest that your child tries reading them with you, and then reads them back to you without your help. It is not necessary to repeat the original words exactly, but your child should understand what the instructions mean. Then leave your child to carry out the first activity alone.

If your child wishes to go on to the next activity immediately, this is fine, but don't insist on it. You may find that the instructions have been read and the activity carried out without you knowing it! This is excellent. Always discuss what your child has done, and give plenty of praise and encouragement.

Your child might like to build up a 'Book of things I have done from my stories'. This would give a sense of achievement and permanence, as well as enabling you to keep a check on development and what has been done.

When all the activities have been done, encourage your child to read the story again before you move on to another book. Your child should now feel secure with it and enjoy reading to you.

Mr Magic

by Helen Arnold

Illustrated by Steve Smallman and Tony Kenyon

A Piccolo Original
In association with Macmillan Education

"I think I'll read this book,"
said Liz.

Mr Magic was a wizard.
But he was a very stupid wizard.
He only knew two spells, and
he had forgotten what the spells did.

One spell was Fee-fi-fo-fum.
The other spell was Abra-ca-da-bra.
Mr Magic went into his den.

"I'll try Fee-fi-fo-fum and
see what happens," said Mr Magic.

An enormous giant jumped out
of the pot.
He was a very bad and wicked giant.

The giant picked up Mr Magic and
walked off with him, taking
enormous steps.

The wicked giant dropped Mr Magic
on top of the highest mountain in the
world . . . and left him there.

"I'll try my other spell and
see what happens," said Mr Magic.

"Abra-ca-da-bra," he said.

A very small dwarf appeared.

"You can choose one of three things,"
said the dwarf.

Marry me . . .

and live happily ever after

Be rich for ever

Have a nice cup of tea

Mr Magic thought hard although
he was very stupid.

"I can't marry the princess because
I have a wife already," he said.

"A box of treasure is not much good
on top of a mountain," said Mr Magic.

"But I would like a nice cup of tea,"
he said.

Just then the dwarf disappeared and
so did the mountain.

Mr Magic found he was back at home.

26

"Hello, dear," he said to his wife.
"I'll save my spells for another day.
What about a nice cup of tea?"

Things to talk about

1. Can you remember the two spells?

What happened when Mr Magic said "Fee-fi-fo-fum"?
What did the giant do?

What happened when Mr Magic said "Abra-ca-da-bra"?
What did the dwarf say?

Which spell did you like best? Why?

2. Make up another word for a spell.
 What do you want to happen when we say it?
 What will happen after that?

Can you write down the spell that you made up?

Looking at pictures and words

1. Write down how many times f comes in

Fee-fi-fo-fum

Write down how many times a comes in

Abra-ca-da-bra

2. Draw three people from the story who fit these words:

<table>
<tr><td>

enormous

wicked

bad

</td><td>

very small

"You can choose."

</td></tr>
</table>

very stupid

thought hard

"I'll save my spells."

3. Copy out this bit of the story. Can you fill in the missing words without looking at the story?

Mr Magic said his first spell. An enormous _____ appeared. He picked up Mr Magic and took him to the _____ of the highest _____ in the _____.

4. What were the three wishes the dwarf gave Mr Magic?

Match these beginnings: with these endings:

Marry me and   cup of tea

Be rich   live happily ever after

Have a nice   for ever

Which wish did Mr Magic choose?

Things to do

What three wishes would you like to come true?
Draw the things you have wished for.

These activities and skills:	will help your children to:
Looking and remembering	hold a story in their heads, retell it in their own words.
Listening, being able to tell the difference between sounds	remember sounds in words and link spoken words with the words they see in print.
Naming things and using different words to explain or retell events	recognise different words in print, build their vocabulary and guess at the meaning of words.
Matching, seeing patterns, similarities and differences	recognise letters, see patterns within words, use the patterns to read 'new' words and split long words into syllables.
Knowing the grammatical patterns of spoken language	guess the word-order in reading.
Anticipating what is likely to happen next in a story	guess what the next sentence or event is likely to be about.
Colouring, getting control of pencils and pens, copying and spelling	produce their own writing, which will help them to understand the way English is written.
Understanding new experiences by linking them to what they already know	read with understanding and think about what they have read.
Understanding their own feelings and those of others	enjoy and respond to stories and identify with the characters.

First published 1989 by Pan Books Ltd, Cavaye Place, London SW10 9PG

9 8 7 6 5 4 3 2 1

Editorial consultant: Donna Bailey

© Pan Books Ltd and Macmillan Publishers Ltd 1989. Text © Helen Arnold 1989

British Library Cataloguing in Publication Data
Arnold, Helen
Mr. Magic.
1. English Readers. – For children
I. Title   II. Series
428.6
ISBN 0–330–30566–2

Printed in Hong Kong